Teddy Bear

by Patricia Chare

Illustrated by Angela Mills

D1510652

Brimax · Newmarket · England

Teddy Bear wakes up. It is not time to get up yet. He looks at his clock and it is only six o'clock. He is warm and snug under his quilt but he knows that something is different about this morning. Something strange has happened, but he is not sure what.

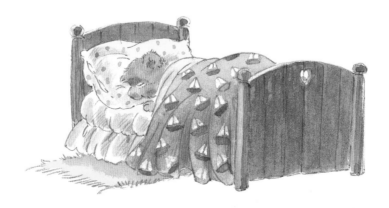

Teddy is afraid to move. What can be wrong? He creeps out of bed quietly, trying not to wake Sally. He tiptoes over to the window, stretches up high and looks out. What a sight!

The garden is all white, as though someone has put a blanket over it. He knows right away what it is, because he has read about it. It is snow! It had fallen silently while they were all asleep.

Teddy is very excited. He has never seen snow before. He shakes Sally and although she is only half awake she climbs out of bed. She goes over to the window to see what Teddy is pointing at. She rubs her eyes and looks out of the window. She gives a gasp of surprise!

"Oh Teddy!" she cries. "There is snow on the ground!"

Both Sally and Teddy are wide awake by now, and they want to go straight out into the snow. They go and wake their parents. Mother says that they must have some breakfast and put some warm clothes on first. They are so excited they cannot wait, but Father says they must.

They eat their breakfast very quickly and then put on their warmest clothes. Finally they are allowed to go outside. Sally stops on the doorstep. "Hurry up, Sally!" says Teddy, trying to get past her. "No," says Sally. "I do not want to ruin the snow. It looks so lovely and smooth."

But Teddy does not mind. Out he goes — Crunch! Crunch! Crunch! He cannot stop. It is such good fun. He runs round and round making patterns in the snow. Teddy sees Spot the dog run out of the house. Spot has not seen snow before either.

Spot stands still and sniffs the cold, white stuff in surprise. His paws are cold. He puts his nose down into the snow and snuffles along trying to smell it. Whatever this is he does not like it. He goes back and sits on the doorstep, where he can keep his eye on things.

Teddy laughs at Spot and calls him over, but Spot will not move. Teddy can see a lump in the snow. What can it be?
He goes over to look. It is round. Teddy brushes some of the snow away. It is his ball.
The snow has covered it up!

"Should we build a snowman?" says Sally.

"Oh yes!" cries Teddy. Their father comes out to help them. Building the snowman takes a long time. Teddy is really enjoying himself and although it is a cold day, they are very hot. Teddy is a bit surprised about this, but his father says it is because they are all working so hard.

When they have finished the snowman, Mother brings out a hat and a scarf for him. They all think he looks very handsome. Sally says that he must have a name. They all suggest a few. Teddy wants to call him Teddy! They eventually decide on Edward.

"I'm cold," says Sally.
"So am I," says Teddy.
Now that they have stopped working their toes and fingers are starting to tingle, and feel very cold. As they stand looking at Edward the snowman, Teddy can feel something very strange touching his head. He looks up into the sky. More snow is falling!

The back door opens and Mother calls, "Come in now. I've made you some hot soup." They all rush inside to get warm. Mother makes them change into some dry, warm clothes before they can drink their soup. "I love soup," says Sally. "So do I," says Teddy. "But I love snow more!" And they all agree.

Say these words again

snug	different
sight	silently
pointing	awake
excited	allowed
outside	laughs
covered	finished